SPIRITUAL JOURNAL

Quarterly Devotional System

by
Dr. Billie Hanks, Jr.
with
Billy Beacham

*"If you are too busy to spend time with God,
you are busier than He intends for you to be."*

Name _____

Address _____

Phone _____

Date: From _____ To _____

A PERSONAL WORD FROM DR. BILLIE HANKS, JR.

I pray this new **Spiritual Journal** will find a natural and exciting place in your walk with Jesus Christ. My own journals have been constant companions through the years. Many of my fondest memories and deepest insights from the Lord are to be found in their pages. If those insights were ever lost, no amount of money could replace them. Their value is not the kind that money can buy.

When the Lord opens a passage in the Bible to your understanding or teaches you some important lesson through the living of life, you are being entrusted with a pearl of great worth. How should you treat such a pearl? For years, I wasted mine. I forgot the good sermons I heard. I lost the fruit of my quiet times. I left behind the priceless insights gained from my spiritual successes and failures.

One day, God used Matthew 7:6 to convict me! *"Give not that which is holy unto the dogs, neither cast ye your pearls before swine."* He made me see that I was no more mature than the foolish Pharisees, who failed to value that which was holy. Like the dogs and the swine of Jesus' parable, I was wasting and abusing His precious pearls!

Why my life felt empty

God brought me to see *why* my life felt empty so much of the time. Why should He bless me, when I took His love and fellowship so lightly? Why should I expect Him to teach me? He knew I would only look forward to the moment of inspiration—never really intending to meditate on my new-found truths or apply them in my daily life.

I began to think I could never break the cycle of spiritual ups and downs. Steady growth seemed impossible! Then slowly but surely things began to change. An older Christian began to disciple me, much as Paul helped young Timothy. He showed me the importance of discipline and showed me how to enjoy consistent fellowship with Christ. Life took on a wonderful new dimension!

A "Quiet Time" made the difference

Like so many other Christians, I was delightfully surprised to discover the great difference a daily "quiet time" could make. I learned firsthand what Moses meant in Psalm 90:14, *"O satisfy us in the morning with Thy lovingkindness, that we may sing for joy and be glad all our days"* (NAS). I experienced His steadfast love in the mornings, and I began to grow.

As time passed, it became natural for me to take notes on my quiet times and the sermons I heard at church. Writing on the back of my bulletin had never been satisfactory, so I began carrying a journal. It grew as I grew, and finally it developed into the **Spiritual Journal** which exists today.

As you begin to use the Quiet Time section, it will also find a special place of importance in your life. When this happens, carefully reserve those special times for fellowship—not work! Your first objective is simply to read your Bible to know God better and experience the joy of His presence.

Be still, as you begin your quiet time. Prepare your heart to listen, and read the Bible expecting a blessing. God will show you more of Himself and His will for your life as He finds that you are *teachable*. Your Quiet Time section is designed to help you grow in that life-changing process. Maturing in Christ comes as the result of our desire to be consistent. Jesus said, *"If ye continue in My Word, then are ye My disciples indeed"* (John 8:31).

Learning to share

As you enjoy the blessings of Bible reading, prayer, Scripture memory, and note taking, remember to *share* what you are learning with others. When Jesus called Andrew and Peter, He said, *"Follow Me, and I will make you become fishers of men"* (Mark 1:17, NAS). The authenticating mark of true discipleship is the love that causes us to witness. Our commission is to reach out. Jesus said, *"Make disciples of all nations . . . teaching them to observe all that I have commanded you; and lo, I am with you always . . ."* (Matthew 28:19-20, NAS).

Jesus has not changed! He is still calling men and women to be His committed disciples, not merely His converts. In that awareness, may we take seriously this clear call to be disciplined followers and walk in the joy of His abundant life.

May God bless you and give you real fulfillment as you participate in personal growth and ministry. I pray that this spiritual aid will prove to be a consistent and inspirational part of your Christian life. Let's covenant together to seek to be fully "usable."

Yours in that expectation,

Billie Hanks, Jr.

"As you therefore have received Christ Jesus the Lord, so walk in Him" (Colossians 2:6, NAS).

ABOUT THE AUTHORS

Dr. Billie Hanks, Jr., is president of the International Evangelism Association, Fort Worth, Texas, and has taught and written widely on spiritual growth. The books he has authored and edited include *My Spiritual Notebook, Discipleship, Everyday Evangelism, Scripture Memory, If You Love Me,* and *The Christian Discipleship Seminar Curriculum.* His books have found popular acceptance with Christian educators, pastors and laypersons.

While serving as minister-at-large for the Billy Graham Evangelistic Association in the late 1970s, Dr. Hanks was the featured speaker for areawide precrusade conferences on discipleship.

He has traveled in sixty-five countries and participated in congresses on world evangelization in Berlin, Lausanne, Singapore, Minneapolis, and Amsterdam. Teaching from an international perspective, Dr. Hanks is frequently invited to minister on university and seminary campuses.

Billy Beacham is vice president for the International Evangelism Association and has authored *Basic Christian Discipleship, Advanced Christian Discipleship,* and the *My Quiet Time* devotional series, as well as other manuals and materials related to youth discipleship and follow-up. A graduate of Southwestern Baptist Theological Seminary, Billy has also led the training program of the youth division of I.E.A. which currently has more than 1000 trained teachers worldwide with more than two thousand participants per month attending their youth seminars.

SPIRITUAL JOURNAL

CONTENTS

I. **QUIET TIME SECTION**

Scriptural insights, prayer requests, personal applications, and memory verses recorded during daily Quiet Time reading

II. **NOTE TAKING SECTION**

Notes taken from sermons, Sunday School lessons, and Bible studies

III. **ADDITIONAL AIDS**

Bible Reading Schedules
Suggested devotional approaches for fast or slow reading

Scripture Memory Review System
A cumulative list of new Scripture memory verses with review chart

New Church Friends List
For new friends and church-related acquaintances

Quiet Time Highlights
Selected insights from your best Quiet Times

Personal Planning Calendars
Month-at-a-glance calendars for ministry activities

Sermon Title Index
A list of current Sermon Titles for easy reference.

HOW TO USE THE QUIET TIME SECTION

"Be still and know that I am God . . ." (Psalm 46:10a, KJV)

1. BEGIN YOUR 15-MINUTE QUIET TIME WITH PRAYER (30 seconds)

   This should be a *brief prayer* for understanding as you prepare to read God's Word.

2. PAUSE FOR MEDITATION (30 seconds)

   Meditate on the meaning of your selected memory verse for the week. Repeat it *out loud* several times, emphasizing the key words which make it meaningful. Seek to find verses that apply to your own spiritual growth. (The shaded space at the top of each Quiet Time page is provided for your new memory verse.)

3. READ THE SCRIPTURES (5 minutes)

   You may choose to use the two helpful *Scripture-reading plans* included in your **Journal**; however, the Quiet Time Section will also work in conjunction with *any other* plan you select. Regardless of the approach you are led to take, remember that consistency and expectancy are the secrets to spiritual growth in personal devotions.

4. RECORD INSIGHTS AND MAKE PERSONAL APPLICATION (3 minutes)

   Think about the meaning of what you read. NOTE: In the example on page 13, you will see several ways you can use *symbols to identify and emphasize items which you wish to recall.*

   To help make a personal application, you might ask these questions (they can be remembered by the acrostic SPACE):*

   Is there a . . .   **Sin** for me to confess?
   Promise for me to claim?
   Attitude for me to change?
   Command for me to obey?
   Example for me to follow?

   *Used by permission, Rick Warren.

   WRITE OUT your thoughts and seek to make your applications PERSONAL, SPECIFIC, and MEASURABLE.

5. SPEND TIME IN PRAYER (2 minutes)

   Ask God to guide you throughout the day and to provide opportunities for you to apply what you have learned during your Quiet Time. Instructions for five important aspects of prayer are on the following pages.

6. REVIEW MEMORY VERSES (4 minutes)

   Review your verses from previous weeks, using the special *Review Section* at the top of your Quiet Time page.

   END YOUR QUIET TIME, BUT CONTINUE THE DAY IN PRAYER.

Scripture Memory Review	Date _Jan. 7 thru 13_
Matt. 6:33	
Josh. 1:8	**Memory Verse for the Week**
Jer. 33:3	1 Peter 1:15 *"but like the Holy One who called you, be holy*
Psa. 46:10	*yourselves also in all your behavior."*
Eph. 6:11	

M ✓ T ✓ W ✓ T ☐ F ☐ S ☐ S ☐

Scriptural Insight

Prayer

MONDAY

✱ 1 Peter 1:13 *"Gird your minds for action"* Don't just slide into the day. Meet it aggressively.

vs. 14 *"former lusts"* Don't fall into the same old sin traps.

m vs. 15 Holiness is our objective.

X 1 Thess. 4:7 *". . . live a holy life."*

P Father, help my mind to stay centered on you today.

C Forgive me for thinking impure thoughts yesterday. Please continue to purify my mind.

Application: I will prepare my mind for Christ-centered thoughts today by meditating on my Quiet Time insights while driving to work rather than listening to the radio.

TUESDAY

→ 1 Peter 2:13 *"Submit . . . to every human institution"* We are to be law-abiding and submissive to those in authority.

✱ vs. 21 *"Christ also suffered . . . leaving an example"* Suffering is evidently part of becoming like our Lord.

C Forgive me for consistently breaking the speed limits.

T Lord, thank You for reminding me that you are not unfamiliar with pain and can fully identify with the times when my body hurts.

Application: Starting today, I will begin driving within the speed limits. Since most of my speeding comes from running late--I will need to plan my schedule better.

WEDNESDAY

✱ 1 Peter 3:15 *"always being ready to make a defense"* I must be prepared to witness on any occasion. This desire will flow out of Christ being Lord in my life.

P Lord, you are aware of my burden for Sam. The last time we talked I couldn't respond to his questions. Please enable me to be prepared for the next opportunity.

Application: This afternoon I will begin committing the Plan of Salvation to memory so I'll be ready when the Lord gives me the opportunity to witness.

✱	my meditation for today	A	Adoration
→	further study needed	C	Confession
x	cross reference	T	Thanksgiving
m	verse(s) to memorize	P	Petition

SCRIPTURE MEMORY

"Thy word have I hid in mine heart, that I might not sin against thee." (Psalm 119:11, KJV)

Normally, references are more easily forgotten than verses. Your review system helps overcome this problem by including spaces for six abbreviated references. Rewrite your references each Monday morning during your Quiet Time. Quote the reference out loud *before* and *after* saying each verse as you review.

A verse is not truly memorized until you *cannot forget it*. Merely learning a verse is not your spiritual objective--live with the verse until it saturates your mind and affects the way you think and act. Good review is the basis for good meditation, and spiritual meditation produces the kind of thinking that builds a godly life. (Philippians 4:8)

Scripture memory requires consistency. Hold yourself accountable by checking the boxes provided by each reference. By simply reviewing each verse for six weeks, you will make a major step toward committing it to memory.

Remember the admonition of Philippians 4:13: *"I can do all things through Christ which strengtheneth me."* *(KJV)* This includes hiding God's Word in your heart!

In this illustration you have already learned five verses and said them out loud three times during the week.

You are now learning Philippians 4:13.

SAMPLE

Scripture Memory Review	Date Jan. 7 thru 13
Matt. 6:33	**Memory Verse for the Week**
Josh. 1:8	Philippians 4:13 *"I can do all things through Christ which*
Jer. 33:3	*strengtheneth me."*
Psa. 46:10	
Eph. 6:11	
M T W T F S S ✓ ✓ ✓ ☐ ☐ ☐ ☐	

ADORATION
(Praising God for Who He is)

"I will bless the Lord at all times; His praise shall continually be in my mouth." (Psalm 34:1, NAS)

There is no better way to *begin* a time of prayer than by expressing praise to God! Praise is the most important element of prayer, and it is probably one of the most neglected. In a prayer of adoration, you express your deep feelings toward God in response to His love, wisdom, presence, power, knowledge, grace, holiness, greatness, and His other divine attributes. This kind of prayer will always be an occasion for "joy"!

As you engage in the school of prayer, remember this important lesson: Our *adoration* must be reserved for God, not for projects, ministries, or works done in His name. When you are in His will, the desire to praise Him will come naturally.

PRAISING GOD IN ADORATION

To help you experience this valuable form of prayer, several choice passages have been listed below.

MAJESTY — 1 Chron. 29:11, Psa. 8:9, Job 37:22
HOLINESS — Ex. 15:11, Isa. 6:3, 1 Pet. 1:14-16

The symbol "A" for "adoration" is used in the code provided in the daily Quiet Time prayer section. As you read, you will find many verses which describe God's divine attributes. Make them the subject of your prayer.

Scriptural Insight		Prayer
➡ I Chron. 29:1-2 Although the temple bore Solomon's name, David actually provided the wealth of materials needed for its construction.	A	Father, I join David this morning in saying that you are the very essence of greatness, power, glory, and victory. Everything everywhere belongs to You--including me.
✱ v. 3 & 9 David gave with joy!		
v. 11 In his prayer of adoration he praised God for His greatness.		

Application:	I will meditate throughout the day upon who God really is, and I will tell Him how proud I am to be His child.

✱	my meditation for today	A	Adoration
➡	further study needed	C	Confession
x	cross reference	T	Thanksgiving
m	verse(s) to memorize	P	Petition

PETITION
(Praying for Your Personal Needs)

"Until now you have asked for nothing in My name; ask, and you will receive, that your joy may be made full." (John 16:24, NAS)

On a day-to-day basis, most of your petitions will deal with small-scale problems, decisions, and opportunities. That is natural, so don't consider your needs beneath God's interest. Remember, Jesus said the Father even knows when a sparrow falls!

Perhaps no verse in the New Testament is as helpful with regard to prayers of petition as John 14:13, in which Jesus said, *"And whatsoever ye shall ask in my name, that will I do, that the Father may be glorified in the Son."* (KJV)

In both large and small requests, the question should always be, "Is my prayer the kind that will *glorify* my heavenly Father?"

Pray about everything, and try not to confuse your *needs* with your *wants*. By faith, be prepared to *praise* Him for a *"yes"* or a *"no"* when He answers your petition. He knows your need, even before you ask. His promise is wonderfully understandable -- *"Seek ye first the kingdom of God, and His righteousness; and all these things shall be added unto you."* (Matthew 6:33, KJV)

BRINGING PETITIONS TO GOD

As you learn to make your requests using the Quiet Time portion of your **Journal**, indicate your petitions with the symbol "P."

	Scriptural Insight		Prayer
→	Titus 1:7-9 The attributes for spiritual leadership are available to everyone, because they are character qualities that can be developed rather than human talents. This is good news!	P	Father, I want very much to have a godly character, so I can be used by You in ministry. Please prepare me for service any way, any time, anywhere.

Application: This week I will ask Ruth Jones and Frank Spencer what they did to develop the godly character which is so obvious in their lives.

*	my meditation for today	A	Adoration
→	further study needed	C	Confession
x	cross reference	T	Thanksgiving
m	verse(s) to memorize	P	Petition

(Left margin: S A M P L E)

CONFESSION
(Agreeing with God about Your Sin)

"If we confess our sins, He is faithful and righteous to forgive us our sins and to cleanse us from all unrighteousness." (1 John 1:9, NAS)

Receiving God's gift of forgiveness is part of the miracle that occurs in a person's life when he accepts Christ as his Savior. Choosing to accept this gift, made possible through the cross, establishes one's eternal *relationship* with God; however, it is our prayer life and obedience that maintain our *fellowship* with Him on a day-to-day basis.

Jesus said, *"If you love Me, you will keep My commandments"* (John 14:15, NAS). When we make self-centered and sinful decisions, our relationship with God remains in effect, but the quality of our fellowship is strained. It is *confession* that restores the privilege of that wonderful fellowship.

HOW TO PRACTICE CONFESSION

As you use the daily Quiet Time portion of your **Journal**, note the single "C," which stands for "confession." A sincere prayer of confession will normally demand that a practical application be made.

Both sin and righteousness are the result of personal decisions, so *confession* that is based upon *genuine repentance* will be proven by a *change* in your daily life. For this reason, your greatest spiritual victories will normally come as the result of this honest, cleansing kind of prayer.

Your confession and repentance need to be *specific*.

Scriptural Insight		Prayer
Eph. 5:15b-16 *"wise, making the most of your time . . ."* Wise people use their time well!	**C**	Lord, I have been wasting a lot of time watching T.V. lately. These are hours I could have spent in Bible reading, prayer, or service. Please forgive my misplaced attention.
✱ vs. 17-20 The secret to using my time well is being controlled by the Holy Spirit.		

Application:
I will cut my T.V. viewing back to five hours per week.

✱	my meditation for today	**A**	Adoration
➜	further study needed	**C**	Confession
x	cross reference	**T**	Thanksgiving
m	verse(s) to memorize	**P**	Petition

THANKSGIVING
(Expressing Gratitude to God for What He Has Done)

"In everything give thanks; for this is God's will for you in Christ Jesus." (1 Thessalonians 5:18, NAS)

The average Christian probably spends too *much* time *asking* and too *little* time *thanking*.

Paul's admonition to *"give thanks in everything"* reflects the maturity of his Christian life. He had been shipwrecked, beaten, hungry, severely criticized, and imprisoned--yet, he could honestly write those words. Why? Because his heart was filled with gratitude! He expressed it like this:

"But whatever things were gain to me, those things I have counted as loss for the sake of Christ. More than that, I count all things to be loss in the view of the surpassing value of knowing Christ Jesus my Lord . . ." (Philippians 3:7-8, NAS)

Prayer provides the opportunity to express our deepest emotions and feelings to God. How long has it been since your heart was overwhelmed with a sense of gratitude?

OFFERING THANKSGIVING IN PRAYER

As you use the Quiet Time section of your **Journal**, simply express the natural appreciation in your heart. To indicate your thanksgiving, write "T" in the margin as your code. Begin thanking God for the things in life which you may have taken for granted. Here are some practical examples:

	Scriptural Insight		Prayer
M	Titus 2:7 *"In all things show yourself to be an example of good deeds . . ."* The ministry of example may be the most important outreach I can have.	T	Lord, as I look back over the years I want to thank You for Sunday School teachers, friends, and family members who have been good examples for me to follow.
	vs. 2-3 Both older men and women are to model the Christian faith for the benefit of younger believers.		
Application:	I will write a thank-you note to Mrs. Dixon and let her know how much her life has meant to me. I will seek to make my own life a positive example to others.		

(left margin: SAMPLE)

*	my meditation for today	A	Adoration
→	further study needed	C	Confession
x	cross reference	T	Thanksgiving
m	verse(s) to memorize	P	Petition

INTERCESSION
(Praying for the Needs of Others)

". . . far be it from me that I should sin against the Lord by ceasing to pray for you." (1 Samuel 12:23, NAS)

When Christ enters our lives, it becomes our spontaneous desire to seek God's blessings for those around us. This is called "intercession."

It would probably be safe to say that the most consistent intercessory praying which we do focuses on the spiritual needs of relatives, friends, and neighbors. Many of those we intercede for are lost. Others are Christians living beneath the resources and privileges freely available to God's children. In each of these instances, intercessory prayer is a ministry of love.

Through intercession, any Christian can be mightily used of God to affect the cause of evangelism worldwide. Whatever our physical condition, we can all be a part of God's powerful army of prayer. Jesus said to His disciples, *"If you abide in Me, and My words abide in you, ask whatever you wish, and it shall be done for you.* (John 15:7, NAS)

INTERCEDING FOR OTHERS

List the names of *individuals* and *ministries* that you desire to pray for. When possible, present their needs to God by name. Pray for them exactly as you would want them to pray for you.

The following pages provide space for each day of the week. The example below shows how to use the code at the bottom of the Intercession pages:

		NAME	SPECIFIC REQUEST
S	L	John	Please show him what drinking will do to his life.
A	F	Dad	Give him wisdom in the job decision he is making.
M			
P	C	Jim	Help him as he shares Christ with his grandmother.
L			
E			

F	Family	- immediate family and other relatives
M	Ministries	- church staff, church services, missionaries and organizations
C	Close Friends	- relationships outside my immediate family
L	Lost Friends	- those who have not yet come to know Christ
G	Government	- local, state, and national officials and agencies

INTERCESSION

	NAME	SPECIFIC REQUEST
D **A** **I** **L** **Y**		
M **O** **N** **D** **A** **Y**		

F	Family	- immediate family and other relatives
M	Ministries	- church staff, church services, Christian leaders and organizations
C	Close Friends	- relationships outside my immediate family
L	Lost Friends	- those who have not yet come to know Christ
G	Government	- local, state, and national officials and agencies

INTERCESSION

NAME	SPECIFIC REQUEST

TUESDAY

WEDNESDAY

QUIET TIME

F	Family	- immediate family and other relatives
M	Ministries	- church staff, church services, Christian leaders and organizations
C	Close Friends	- relationships outside my immediate family
L	Lost Friends	- those who have not yet come to know Christ
G	Government	- local, state, and national officials and agencies

INTERCESSION

	NAME	SPECIFIC REQUEST
T H U R S D A Y		
F R I D A Y		

F	Family	- immediate family and other relatives
M	Ministries	- church staff, church services, Christian leaders and organizations
C	Close Friends	- relationships outside my immediate family
L	Lost Friends	- those who have not yet come to know Christ
G	Government	- local, state, and national officials and agencies

INTERCESSION

	NAME	SPECIFIC REQUEST
SATURDAY		
SUNDAY		

F	Family	- immediate family and other relatives
M	Ministries	- church staff, church services, Christian leaders and organizations
C	Close Friends	- relationships outside my immediate family
L	Lost Friends	- those who have not yet come to know Christ
G	Government	- local, state, and national officials and agencies

SPECIAL PRAYER

DATE	PRAYER	DATE ANSWERED

SPECIAL PRAYER

DATE	PRAYER	DATE ANSWERED

Scripture Memory Review

_____
_____
_____
_____

M T W T F S S
☐ ☐ ☐ ☐ ☐ ☐ ☐

Date _____

Memory Verse for the Week

_____
_____
_____
_____
_____

Scriptural Insight   **Prayer**

MONDAY

Application:

TUESDAY

Application:

WEDNESDAY

Application:

✳ my meditation for today	A Adoration
→ further study needed	C Confession
x cross reference	T Thanksgiving
m verse(s) to memorize	P Petition

THURSDAY

Application:

FRIDAY

Application:

SATURDAY

Application:

SUNDAY

Application:

Date _____

Memory Verse for the Week

_____
_____
_____
_____

Scriptural Insight   **Prayer**

M O N D A Y

Application:

T U E S D A Y

Application:

W E D N E S D A Y

Application:

✱ my meditation for today	**A** Adoration
➜ further study needed	**C** Confession
x cross reference	**T** Thanksgiving
m verse(s) to memorize	**P** Petition

THURSDAY

Application:

FRIDAY

Application:

SATURDAY

Application:

SUNDAY

Application:

Scripture Memory Review	Date _____
_____	**Memory Verse for the Week**

M T W T F S S
☐ ☐ ☐ ☐ ☐ ☐ ☐

Scriptural Insight	**Prayer**

MONDAY

Application:

TUESDAY

Application:

WEDNESDAY

Application:

*	my meditation for today	A	Adoration
→	further study needed	C	Confession
x	cross reference	T	Thanksgiving
m	verse(s) to memorize	P	Petition

Application:

Application:

Application:

Application:

Scripture Memory Review

_____
_____
_____
_____

M T W T F S S
☐ ☐ ☐ ☐ ☐ ☐ ☐

Date _____

Memory Verse for the Week

_____
_____
_____
_____

Scriptural Insight	Prayer

MONDAY

Application:

TUESDAY

Application:

WEDNESDAY

Application:

✱ my meditation for today	A Adoration
→ further study needed	C Confession
x cross reference	T Thanksgiving
m verse(s) to memorize	P Petition

THURSDAY

Application:

FRIDAY

Application:

SATURDAY

Application:

SUNDAY

Application:

QUIET TIME

Date _____

Memory Verse for the Week

M T W T F S S

Scriptural Insight

Prayer

MONDAY

Application:

TUESDAY

Application:

WEDNESDAY

Application:

* my meditation for today	A Adoration
→ further study needed	C Confession
x cross reference	T Thanksgiving
m verse(s) to memorize	P Petition

Application:

Application:

Application:

Application:

THURSDAY

Application:

FRIDAY

Application:

SATURDAY

Application:

SUNDAY

Application:

Date _____

Memory Verse for the Week

_____
_____
_____
_____

Scriptural Insight   **Prayer**

**M
O
N
D
A
Y**

Application:

**T
U
E
S
D
A
Y**

Application:

**W
E
D
N
E
S
D
A
Y**

Application:

✱	my meditation for today	A	Adoration
→	further study needed	C	Confession
x	cross reference	T	Thanksgiving
m	verse(s) to memorize	P	Petition

THURSDAY

Application:

FRIDAY

Application:

SATURDAY

Application:

Application:

Date _____

Memory Verse for the Week

_____
_____
_____
_____

Scriptural Insight	**Prayer**

M O N D A Y

Application:

T U E S D A Y

Application:

W E D N E S D A Y

Application:

✱ my meditation for today	**A** Adoration
➜ further study needed	**C** Confession
x cross reference	**T** Thanksgiving
m verse(s) to memorize	**P** Petition

THURSDAY

Application:

FRIDAY

Application:

SATURDAY

Application:

SUNDAY

Application:

Scripture Memory Review	Date _____
_____	**Memory Verse for the Week**
_____	_____
_____	_____
_____	_____
M T W T F S S	_____
☐ ☐ ☐ ☐ ☐ ☐ ☐	_____

Scriptural Insight   **Prayer**

MONDAY

Application:

TUESDAY

Application:

WEDNESDAY

Application:

✱ my meditation for today	**A** Adoration
→ further study needed	**C** Confession
x cross reference	**T** Thanksgiving
m verse(s) to memorize	**P** Petition

THURSDAY

Application:

FRIDAY

Application:

SATURDAY

Application:

SUNDAY

Application:

Scripture Memory Review	Date _____
_____	**Memory Verse for the Week**
_____	_____
_____	_____
_____	_____
M T W T F S S	_____
☐ ☐ ☐ ☐ ☐ ☐ ☐	_____

Scriptural Insight   **Prayer**

MONDAY

Application:

TUESDAY

Application:

WEDNESDAY

Application:

✱	my meditation for today	A	Adoration
➜	further study needed	C	Confession
x	cross reference	T	Thanksgiving
m	verse(s) to memorize	P	Petition

Application:

Application:

Application:

Application:

Date _____

Memory Verse for the Week

_____

_____

_____

_____

Scriptural Insight   **Prayer**

MONDAY

Application:

TUESDAY

Application:

WEDNESDAY

Application:

✳ my meditation for today	A Adoration
➙ further study needed	C Confession
x cross reference	T Thanksgiving
m verse(s) to memorize	P Petition

THURSDAY

Application:

FRIDAY

Application:

Application:

Application:

Date _____

Memory Verse for the Week

_____

_____

_____

_____

_____

Scriptural Insight	Prayer

MONDAY

Application:

TUESDAY

Application:

WEDNESDAY

Application:

* my meditation for today	**A** Adoration
➔ further study needed	**C** Confession
x cross reference	**T** Thanksgiving
m verse(s) to memorize	**P** Petition

THURSDAY

Application:

FRIDAY

Application:

SATURDAY

Application:

SUNDAY

Application:

Date _____

Memory Verse for the Week

_____

_____

_____

_____

Scriptural Insight	Prayer

MONDAY

Application:

TUESDAY

Application:

WEDNESDAY

Application:

✱	my meditation for today	A	Adoration
→	further study needed	C	Confession
x	cross reference	T	Thanksgiving
m	verse(s) to memorize	P	Petition

THURSDAY

Application:

FRIDAY

Application:

SATURDAY

Application:

SUNDAY

Application:

NOTE TAKING
SECTION II

USE YOUR NOTE TAKING SECTION DURING:

Worship Services
Evangelistic Meetings
Group Bible Studies
Bible Conferences

The **Journal's** approach to note taking is simplified through the use of symbols. When God impresses you with a thought during any part of a sermon, just write it down, code it, and continue note taking. After several weeks, you will become familiar with the symbols. At the end of each message, it will be easy to refer back to the subject areas which have been coded.

Explanation of Symbols:

✳ *Point to Remember:* This could be an outstanding quote, a profound statement, or a new insight from God's Word.

→ *Further Study Needed:* When you find a passage or thought of particular interest which you would like to study in more detail, code it with an "→". If the word or passage is unclear, use the same code.

✓ *Illustration:* Summarize good illustrations so you can remember them. You will find that the illustrations God uses to convict or challenge you will often communicate with others as well.

X *Cross Reference:* Many times a speaker will refer to related verses in the Bible. In such cases, use an "X" to code those references. As you become increasingly acquainted with the Scriptures, God will begin bringing references to your mind as you listen to His Word.

○ *Application:* Applying God's Word is the most important principle in living the Christian life. To *emphasize* areas for application, code your notes with a circle, "○". Notice in the example how the application portions of the notes are circled, as well as coded. You will usually find it necessary to write out *specific steps* to put your application into immediate practice. Your applications need to be:

PERSONAL: Select an activity *you* can do!
SPECIFIC: Be *detailed* and *realistic*!
MEASURABLE: Give yourself a *time limit*!

"Discipline yourself for the purpose of godliness" (1 Timothy 4:7b, NAS).

CODE		
✳ point to remember		
✓ illustration	Jan. 16	
✗ cross reference	_date_	☑ Sermon
→ further study needed	Rev. Jones · · · · · · · 1 John 5:11-12	☐ Sunday School
○ personal application	_speaker_ _text_	☐ Bible Study
	Knowing God	☐ Book Review
	subject/title	☐ Cassette Tape

". . . God has given us eternal life, and this life is in His Son."
— v. 11

✳ To receive Christ is to begin an eternal relationship with God.

→ "He who has the Son has life. He who does not have the Son of
God does not have life." — v. 12.

○ (Lord, I thank you for the eternal life that you have given me.)

✳ All men are either saved or lost. There is no middle ground!

✓ Salvation resembles marriage. If I ask, "Are you married?" you
would not answer, "I hope so," or "Maybe so." Only one of
two answers could be correct: "Yes," or "No." The same is
true with salvation. Either we have invited Jesus Christ into our
hearts as Savior, or we have not.

m
✗ Jesus said, "I am the way, the truth, and the life. No man
comes unto the Father but by Me" (John 14:6). Christ is the
only way to heaven!

The message of Christianity is unique. Jesus did not claim to be
one prophet among many. He claimed to be the only Savior.
Because of His death on the cross on our behalf, we can choose
to know God as our Father, rather than our judge.

✳ Every year millions of people die with no knowledge of Jesus
Christ.

○ (I need to develop a deeper burden for non-Christians.)

○ (This week I will talk to John Doe about what it means to be a
Christian.)

". . . Faith cometh by hearing . . ."

NOTE TAKING

date _____

speaker _____   text _____

subject/title _____

☐ Sermon
☐ Sunday School
☐ Bible Study
☐ Book Review
☐ Cassette Tape

"... Faith cometh by hearing ..."

CODE

* point to remember
✓ illustration
✗ cross reference
→ further study needed
○ personal application

_____ date _____

☐ Sermon
☐ Sunday School
☐ Bible Study
☐ Book Review
☐ Cassette Tape

speaker _____ text _____

_____ subject/title _____

CODE
* point to remember
✓ illustration
X cross reference
→ further study needed
○ personal application

_____ date

speaker _____ _____ text

_____ subject/title

☐ Sermon
☐ Sunday School
☐ Bible Study
☐ Book Review
☐ Cassette Tape

CODE

✳ point to remember
✓ illustration
✗ cross reference
→ further study needed
○ personal application

date

speaker   text

subject/title

☐ Sermon
☐ Sunday School
☐ Bible Study
☐ Book Review
☐ Cassette Tape

NOTE TAKING

"... Faith cometh by hearing ..."

_____
date

☐ Sermon
☐ Sunday School
☐ Bible Study
☐ Book Review
☐ Cassette Tape

speaker _____ _____ text

subject/title _____

"... Faith cometh by hearing ..."

date _____

speaker _____   text _____

subject/title _____

☐ Sermon
☐ Sunday School
☐ Bible Study
☐ Book Review
☐ Cassette Tape

NOTE TAKING

". . . Faith cometh by hearing . . ."

CODE
* point to remember
✓ illustration
X cross reference
→ further study needed
○ personal application

_____ date _____

□ Sermon
□ Sunday School
□ Bible Study
□ Book Review
□ Cassette Tape

speaker _____   _____ text

_____ subject/title _____

". . . Faith cometh by hearing . . ."

CODE

✳ point to remember
✓ illustration
✗ cross reference
→ further study needed
○ personal application

date

speaker _____ text

subject/title

☐ Sermon
☐ Sunday School
☐ Bible Study
☐ Book Review
☐ Cassette Tape

NOTE TAKING

". . . Faith cometh by hearing . . ."

date _____

□ Sermon
□ Sunday School
□ Bible Study
□ Book Review
□ Cassette Tape

speaker _____   text _____

subject/title _____

". . . Faith cometh by hearing . . ."

CODE

※ point to remember
✓ illustration
✗ cross reference
→ further study needed
○ personal application

_____
date

speaker _____ _____ text

_____
subject/title

☐ Sermon
☐ Sunday School
☐ Bible Study
☐ Book Review
☐ Cassette Tape

". . . Faith cometh by hearing . . ."

CODE

＊ point to remember
✔ illustration
✕ cross reference
→ further study needed
○ personal application

_____
date

speaker _____ _____ text

_____
subject/title

☐ Sermon
☐ Sunday School
☐ Bible Study
☐ Book Review
☐ Cassette Tape

CODE
* point to remember
✓ illustration
✗ cross reference
→ further study needed
○ personal application

date _____

speaker _____ text _____

subject/title _____

☐ Sermon
☐ Sunday School
☐ Bible Study
☐ Book Review
☐ Cassette Tape

". . . Faith cometh by hearing . . ."

CODE

✳ point to remember
✓ illustration
✗ cross reference
➔ further study needed
○ personal application

_____
date

speaker _____ _____ text

_____
subject/title

☐ Sermon
☐ Sunday School
☐ Bible Study
☐ Book Review
☐ Cassette Tape

"... Faith cometh by hearing ..."

CODE

＊ point to remember
✓ illustration
✗ cross reference
→ further study needed
○ personal application

_____
date

speaker _____   _____ text

_____
subject/title

☐ **Sermon**
☐ **Sunday School**
☐ **Bible Study**
☐ **Book Review**
☐ **Cassette Tape**

NOTE TAKING

". . . Faith cometh by hearing . . ."

_____ date

_____ _____
speaker   text

_____
subject/title

☐ Sermon
☐ Sunday School
☐ Bible Study
☐ Book Review
☐ Cassette Tape

". . . Faith cometh by hearing . . ."

CODE
* point to remember
✓ illustration
✗ cross reference
→ further study needed
○ personal application

_____ date _____

speaker _____ text _____

subject/title _____

☐ Sermon
☐ Sunday School
☐ Bible Study
☐ Book Review
☐ Cassette Tape

NOTE TAKING

"... Faith cometh by hearing ..."

CODE

✳ point to remember
✓ illustration
✗ cross reference
→ further study needed
○ personal application

_____
date

speaker _____ _____ text

□ Sermon
□ Sunday School
□ Bible Study
□ Book Review
□ Cassette Tape

_____
subject/title

CODE

✳ point to remember
✓ illustration
✗ cross reference
→ further study needed
○ personal application

_____ date

speaker _____ _____ text

_____
subject/title

☐ Sermon
☐ Sunday School
☐ Bible Study
☐ Book Review
☐ Cassette Tape

NOTE TAKING

CODE

✳ point to remember
✓ illustration
✗ cross reference
→ further study needed
○ personal application

_____ date

speaker _____ _____ text

_____
subject/title

☐ **Sermon**
☐ **Sunday School**
☐ **Bible Study**
☐ **Book Review**
☐ **Cassette Tape**

". . . Faith cometh by hearing . . ."

CODE

※ point to remember
✓ illustration
✗ cross reference
→ further study needed
○ personal application

_____ date
speaker _____ text
_____ subject/title

☐ **Sermon**
☐ **Sunday School**
☐ **Bible Study**
☐ **Book Review**
☐ **Cassette Tape**

NOTE TAKING

". . . Faith cometh by hearing . . ."

date

speaker   text

□ Sermon
□ Sunday School
□ Bible Study
□ Book Review
□ Cassette Tape

subject/title

". . . Faith cometh by hearing . . ."

CODE

※ point to remember
✓ illustration
✗ cross reference
→ further study needed
○ personal application

_____ date

speaker _____ text _____

_____ subject/title

☐ Sermon
☐ Sunday School
☐ Bible Study
☐ Book Review
☐ Cassette Tape

NOTE TAKING

"... Faith cometh by hearing ..."

CODE

＊ point to remember
✓ illustration
✗ cross reference
→ further study needed
○ personal application

date _____

speaker _____   text _____

subject/title _____

☐ Sermon
☐ Sunday School
☐ Bible Study
☐ Book Review
☐ Cassette Tape

". . . Faith cometh by hearing . . ."

CODE

✳ point to remember
✓ illustration
✗ cross reference
→ further study needed
○ personal application

_____ date _____

speaker _____ | _____ text

_____ subject/title _____

☐ Sermon
☐ Sunday School
☐ Bible Study
☐ Book Review
☐ Cassette Tape

NOTE TAKING

". . . Faith cometh by hearing . . ."

CODE

✳ point to remember
✓ illustration
✗ cross reference
→ further study needed
○ personal application

date _____

speaker _____   text _____

subject/title _____

☐ Sermon
☐ Sunday School
☐ Bible Study
☐ Book Review
☐ Cassette Tape

CODE

✳ point to remember
✓ illustration
✗ cross reference
→ further study needed
○ personal application

_____
date

_____   _____
speaker   text

_____
subject/title

☐ **Sermon**
☐ **Sunday School**
☐ **Bible Study**
☐ **Book Review**
☐ **Cassette Tape**

NOTE TAKING

". . . Faith cometh by hearing . . ."

CODE
* ✳ point to remember
* ✓ illustration
* ✗ cross reference
* → further study needed
* ○ personal application

_____ date

speaker _____ _____ text

_____
subject/title

- ☐ Sermon
- ☐ Sunday School
- ☐ Bible Study
- ☐ Book Review
- ☐ Cassette Tape

". . . Faith cometh by hearing . . ."

CODE

* point to remember
✓ illustration
✗ cross reference
→ further study needed
○ personal application

_____ date _____

speaker _____ text

_____ subject/title _____

☐ Sermon
☐ Sunday School
☐ Bible Study
☐ Book Review
☐ Cassette Tape

"... Faith cometh by hearing ..."

_____ date _____

speaker _____ _____ text

_____ subject/title _____

☐ Sermon
☐ Sunday School
☐ Bible Study
☐ Book Review
☐ Cassette Tape

". . . Faith cometh by hearing . . ."

CODE

✻ point to remember
✓ illustration
✗ cross reference
→ further study needed
○ personal application

_____ date _____

speaker _____ text _____

_____ subject/title _____

☐ Sermon
☐ Sunday School
☐ Bible Study
☐ Book Review
☐ Cassette Tape

NOTE TAKING

". . . Faith cometh by hearing . . ."

date

speaker _____ text

subject/title

☐ Sermon
☐ Sunday School
☐ Bible Study
☐ Book Review
☐ Cassette Tape

CODE

❋ point to remember
✓ illustration
✗ cross reference
→ further study needed
○ personal application

_____
date

☐ Sermon
☐ Sunday School
☐ Bible Study
☐ Book Review
☐ Cassette Tape

speaker _____ text

_____
subject/title

NOTE TAKING

". . . Faith cometh by hearing . . ."

CODE

✳ point to remember
✓ illustration
✗ cross reference
→ further study needed
○ personal application

_____ date _____

speaker _____ text _____

_____ subject/title _____

☐ Sermon
☐ Sunday School
☐ Bible Study
☐ Book Review
☐ Cassette Tape

CODE
* point to remember
✓ illustration
✗ cross reference
→ further study needed
○ personal application

date _____

speaker _____ text _____

subject/title _____

☐ Sermon
☐ Sunday School
☐ Bible Study
☐ Book Review
☐ Cassette Tape

NOTE TAKING

". . . Faith cometh by hearing . . ."

CODE

※ point to remember
✓ illustration
✗ cross reference
→ further study needed
○ personal application

_____ date _____ ☐ Sermon
                                        ☐ Sunday School
speaker _____ | _____ text   ☐ Bible Study
                                        ☐ Book Review
_____ subject/title _____   ☐ Cassette Tape

CODE		
✳	point to remember	
✓	illustration	
✗	cross reference	
→	further study needed	
○	personal application	

_____ date _____

☐ Sermon
☐ Sunday School
speaker _____ text ☐ Bible Study
☐ Book Review
_____ subject/title _____ ☐ Cassette Tape

NOTE TAKING

" . . . Faith cometh by hearing . . ."

_____

date

☐ Sermon

☐ Sunday School

_____ _____

speaker   text

☐ Bible Study

☐ Book Review

_____

subject/title

☐ Cassette Tape

"... Faith cometh by hearing ..."

date _____

speaker _____ text _____

subject/title _____

☐ Sermon
☐ Sunday School
☐ Bible Study
☐ Book Review
☐ Cassette Tape

NOTE TAKING

". . . Faith cometh by hearing . . ."

date _____

speaker _____ text _____

subject/title _____

☐ Sermon
☐ Sunday School
☐ Bible Study
☐ Book Review
☐ Cassette Tape

"... Faith cometh by hearing ..."

CODE

✳ point to remember
✓ illustration
✗ cross reference
→ further study needed
○ personal application

date _____

speaker _____ text _____

subject/title _____

☐ Sermon
☐ Sunday School
☐ Bible Study
☐ Book Review
☐ Cassette Tape

NOTE TAKING

"... Faith cometh by hearing ..."

BIBLE READING SCHEDULE

To effectively use the Quiet Time portion of your devotional guide, it is necessary to have a plan for consistent daily Bible reading. Plan to read at a pace that is comfortable for you. Strive for understanding and not just quantity.

If you decide to read the Bible through in a year, you may choose to read from the Old Testament in the mornings and from the New Testament in the evenings.

If you prefer reading at a slower pace, try reading only the New Testament passage each morning. This will require only *20 to 25 verses* per day!

JANUARY

DATE	MORNING		EVENING	
1	GEN.	1,2	MATT.	1
2	GEN.	3,4,5	MATT.	2
3	GEN.	6,7,8	MATT.	3
4	GEN.	9,10,11	MATT.	4
5	GEN.	12,13,14	MATT.	5:1-26
6	GEN.	15,16,17	MATT.	5:27-48
7	GEN.	18,19	MATT.	6
8	GEN.	20,21,22	MATT.	7
9	GEN.	23,24	MATT.	8
10	GEN.	25,26	MATT.	9:1-17
11	GEN.	27,28	MATT.	9:18-38
12	GEN.	29,30	MATT.	10:1-23
13	GEN.	31,32	MATT.	10:24-42
14	GEN.	33,34,35	MATT.	11
15	GEN.	36,37	MATT.	12:1-21
16	GEN.	38,39,40	MATT.	12:22-50
17	GEN.	41	MATT.	13:1-32
18	GEN.	42,43	MATT.	13:33-58
19	GEN.	44,45	MATT.	14:1-21
20	GEN.	46,47,48	MATT.	14:22-36
21	GEN.	49,50	MATT.	15:1-20
22	EXOD.	1,2,3	MATT.	15:21-39
23	EXOD.	4,5,6	MATT.	16
24	EXOD.	7,8	MATT.	17
25	EXOD.	9,10	MATT.	18:1-20
26	EXOD.	11,12	MATT.	18:21-35
27	EXOD.	13,14,15	MATT.	19:1-15
28	EXOD.	16,17,18	MATT.	19:16-30
29	EXOD.	19,20,21	MATT.	20:1-16
30	EXOD.	22,23,24	MATT.	20:17-34
31	EXOD.	25,26	MATT.	21:1-22

FEBRUARY

DATE	MORNING		EVENING	
1	EXOD.	27,28	MATT.	21:23-46
2	EXOD.	29,30	MATT.	22:1-22
3	EXOD.	31,32,33	MATT.	22:23-46
4	EXOD.	34,35,36	MATT.	23:1-22
5	EXOD.	37,38	MATT.	23:23-39
6	EXOD.	39,40	MATT.	24:1-22
7	LEV.	1,2,3	MATT.	24:23-51
8	LEV.	4,5,6	MATT.	25:1-30
9	LEV.	7,8,9	MATT.	25:31-46
10	LEV.	10,11,12	MATT.	26:1-19
11	LEV.	13	MATT.	26:20-54
12	LEV.	14	MATT.	26:55-75
13	LEV.	15,16,17	MATT.	27:1-31
14	LEV.	18,19	MATT.	27:32-66
15	LEV.	20,21	MATT.	28:1-20
16	LEV.	22,23	MARK	1:1-22
17	LEV.	24,25	MARK	1:23-45
18	LEV.	26,27	MARK	2
19	NUM.	1,2	MARK	3:1-21
20	NUM.	3,4	MARK	3:22-35
21	NUM.	5,6	MARK	4:1-20

FEBRUARY (continued)

DATE	MORNING		EVENING	
22	NUM.	7	MARK	4:21-41
23	NUM.	8,9,10	MARK	5:1-20
24	NUM.	11,12,13	MARK	5:21-43
25	NUM.	14,15	MARK	6:1-32
26	NUM.	16,17	MARK	6:33-56
27	NUM.	18,19,20	MARK	7:1-13
28	NUM.	21,22	MARK	7:14-37
29	NUM.	23,24,25	MARK	8:1-21

Divide chapters for Feb. 29 and read them Feb. 28 and Mar. 1 when Feb. has only 28 days.

MARCH

DATE	MORNING		EVENING	
1	NUM.	26,27	MARK	8:22-38
2	NUM.	28,29	MARK	9:1-29
3	NUM.	30,31	MARK	9:30-50
4	NUM.	32,33	MARK	10:1-31
5	NUM.	34,35,36	MARK	10:32-52
6	DEUT.	1,2	MARK	11:1-19
7	DEUT.	3,4	MARK	11:20-33
8	DEUT.	5,6,7	MARK	12:1-27
9	DEUT.	8,9,10	MARK	12:28-44
10	DEUT.	11,12,13	MARK	13:1-13
11	DEUT.	14,15,16	MARK	13:14-37
12	DEUT.	17,18,19	MARK	14:1-25
13	DEUT.	20,21,22	MARK	14:26-50
14	DEUT.	23,24,25	MARK	14:51-72
15	DEUT.	26,27	MARK	15:1-26
16	DEUT.	28	MARK	15:27-47
17	DEUT.	29,30	MARK	16
18	DEUT.	31,32	LUKE	1:1-23
19	DEUT.	33,34	LUKE	1:24-56
20	JOSH.	1,2,3	LUKE	1:57-80
21	JOSH.	4,5,6	LUKE	2:1-24
22	JOSH.	7,8	LUKE	2:25-52
23	JOSH.	9,10	LUKE	3
24	JOSH.	11,12,13	LUKE	4:1-32
25	JOSH.	14,15	LUKE	4:33-44
26	JOSH.	16,17,18	LUKE	5:1-16
27	JOSH.	19,20	LUKE	5:17-39
28	JOSH.	21,22	LUKE	6:1-26
29	JOSH.	23,24	LUKE	6:27-49
30	JUDG.	1,2	LUKE	7:1-30
31	JUDG.	3,4,5	LUKE	7:31-50

APRIL

DATE	MORNING		EVENING	
1	JUDG.	6,7	LUKE	8:1-21
2	JUDG.	8,9	LUKE	8:22-56
3	JUDG.	10,11	LUKE	9:1-36
4	JUDG.	12,13,14	LUKE	9:37-62
5	JUDG.	15,16,17	LUKE	10:1-24
6	JUDG.	18,19	LUKE	10:25-42
7	JUDG.	20,21	LUKE	11:1-28
8	RUTH		LUKE	11:29-54
9	I SAM.	1,2,3	LUKE	12:1-34
10	I SAM.	4,5,6	LUKE	12:35-59
11	I SAM.	7,8,9	LUKE	13:1-21
12	I SAM.	10,11,12	LUKE	13:22-35

APRIL (continued)

DATE	MORNING		EVENING	
13	I SAM.	13,14	LUKE	14:1-24
14	I SAM.	15,16	LUKE	14:25-35
15	I SAM.	17,18	LUKE	15:1-10
16	I SAM.	19,20,21	LUKE	15:11-32
17	I SAM.	22,23,24	LUKE	16:1-18
18	I SAM.	25,26	LUKE	16:19-31
19	I SAM.	27,28,29	LUKE	17:1-19
20	I SAM.	30,31	LUKE	17:20-37
21	II SAM.	1,2,3	LUKE	18:1-17
22	II SAM.	4,5,6	LUKE	18:18-43
23	II SAM.	7,8,9	LUKE	19:1-28
24	II SAM.	10,11,12	LUKE	19:29-48
25	II SAM.	13,14	LUKE	20:1-26
26	II SAM.	15,16	LUKE	20:27-47
27	II SAM.	17,18	LUKE	21:1-19
28	II SAM.	19,20	LUKE	21:20-38
29	II SAM.	21,22	LUKE	22:1-30
30	II SAM.	23,24	LUKE	22:31-53

MAY

DATE	MORNING		EVENING	
1	I KINGS	1,2	LUKE	22:54-71
2	I KINGS	3,4,5	LUKE	23:1-26
3	I KINGS	6,7	LUKE	23:27-38
4	I KINGS	8,9	LUKE	23:39-56
5	I KINGS	10,11	LUKE	24:1-35
6	I KINGS	12,13	LUKE	24:36-53
7	I KINGS	14,15	JOHN	1:1-28
8	I KINGS	16,17,18	JOHN	1:29-51
9	I KINGS	19,20	JOHN	2
10	I KINGS	21,22	JOHN	3:1-21
11	II KINGS	1,2,3	JOHN	3:22-36
12	II KINGS	4,5	JOHN	4:1-30
13	II KINGS	6,7,8	JOHN	4:31-54
14	II KINGS	9,10,11	JOHN	5:1-24
15	II KINGS	12,13,14	JOHN	5:25-47
16	II KINGS	15,16,17	JOHN	6:1-21
17	II KINGS	18,19	JOHN	6:22-44
18	II KINGS	20,21,22	JOHN	6:45-71
19	II KINGS	23,24,25	JOHN	7:1-31
20	I CHRON.	1,2	JOHN	7:32-53
21	I CHRON.	3,4,5	JOHN	8:1-20
22	I CHRON.	6,7	JOHN	8:21-36
23	I CHRON.	8,9,10	JOHN	8:37-59
24	I CHRON.	11,12,13	JOHN	9:1-23
25	I CHRON.	14,15,16	JOHN	9:24-41
26	I CHRON.	17,18,19	JOHN	10:1-21
27	I CHRON.	20,21,22	JOHN	10:22-42
28	I CHRON.	23,24,25	JOHN	11:1-17
29	I CHRON.	26,27	JOHN	11:18-46
30	I CHRON.	28,29	JOHN	11:47-57
31	II CHRON.	1,2,3	JOHN	12:1-19

JUNE

DATE	MORNING		EVENING	
1	II CHR.	4,5,6	JOHN	12:20-50
2	II CHR.	7,8,9	JOHN	13:1-17
3	II CHR.	10,11,12	JOHN	13:18-38
4	II CHR.	13-16	JOHN	14
5	II CHR.	17,18,19	JOHN	15
6	II CHR.	20,21,22	JOHN	16:1-15
7	II CHR.	23,24,25	JOHN	16:16-33
8	II CHR.	26,27,28	JOHN	17
9	II CHR.	29,30,31	JOHN	18:1-23
10	II CHR.	32,33	JOHN	18:24-40
11	II CHR.	34,35,36	JOHN	19:1-22
12	EZRA	1,2	JOHN	19:23-42
13	EZRA	3,4,5	JOHN	20
14	EZRA	6,7,8	JOHN	21
15	EZRA	9,10	ACTS	1
16	NEH.	1,2,3	ACTS	2:1-13
17	NEH.	4,5,6	ACTS	2:14-47
18	NEH.	7,8	ACTS	3
19	NEH.	9,10,11	ACTS	4:1-22
20	NEH.	12,13	ACTS	4:23-37
21	ESTHER	1,2,3	ACTS	5:1-16

JUNE (continued)

DATE	MORNING		EVENING	
22	ESTHER	4,5,6	ACTS	5:17-42
23	ESTHER	7-10	ACTS	6
24	JOB	1,2,3	ACTS	7:1-19
25	JOB	4,5,6	ACTS	7:20-43
26	JOB	7,8,9	ACTS	7:44-60
27	JOB	10,11,12	ACTS	8:1-25
28	JOB	13,14,15	ACTS	8:26-40
29	JOB	16,17,18	ACTS	9:1-22
30	JOB	19,20	ACTS	9:23-43

JULY

DATE	MORNING		EVENING	
1	JOB	21,22	ACTS	10:1-23
2	JOB	23,24,25	ACTS	10:24-48
3	JOB	26,27,28	ACTS	11
4	JOB	29,30	ACTS	12
5	JOB	31,32	ACTS	13:1-23
6	JOB	33,34	ACTS	13:24-52
7	JOB	35,36,37	ACTS	14
8	JOB	38,39	ACTS	15:1-21
9	JOB	40,41,42	ACTS	15:22-41
10	PS.	1,2,3	ACTS	16:1-15
11	PS.	4,5,6	ACTS	16:16-40
12	PS.	7,8,9	ACTS	17:1-15
13	PS.	10,11,12	ACTS	17:16-34
14	PS.	13-16	ACTS	18
15	PS.	17,18	ACTS	19:1-20
16	PS.	19,20,21	ACTS	19:21-41
17	PS.	22,23,24	ACTS	20:1-16
18	PS.	25,26,27	ACTS	20:17-38
19	PS.	28,29,30	ACTS	21:1-14
20	PS.	31,32,33	ACTS	21:15-40
21	PS.	34,35	ACTS	22
22	PS.	36,37	ACTS	23:1-11
23	PS.	38,39,40	ACTS	23:12-35
24	PS.	41,42,43	ACTS	24
25	PS.	44,45,46	ACTS	25
26	PS.	47,48,49	ACTS	26
27	PS.	50,51,52	ACTS	27:1-25
28	PS.	53,54,55	ACTS	27:26-44
29	PS.	56,57,58	ACTS	28:1-15
30	PS.	59,60,61	ACTS	28:16-31
31	PS.	62,63,64	ROM.	1

AUGUST

DATE	MORNING		EVENING	
1	PS.	65,66,67	ROM.	2
2	PS.	68,69	ROM.	3
3	PS.	70,71,72	ROM.	4
4	PS.	73,74	ROM.	5
5	PS.	75,76,77	ROM.	6
6	PS.	78	ROM.	7
7	PS.	79,80,81	ROM.	8:1-18
8	PS.	82,83,84	ROM.	8:19-39
9	PS.	85,86,87	ROM.	9
10	PS.	88,89	ROM.	10
11	PS.	90,91,92	ROM.	11:1-21
12	PS.	93,94,95	ROM.	11:22-36
13	PS.	96,97,98	ROM.	12
14	PS.	99-102	ROM.	13
15	PS.	103,104	ROM.	14
16	PS.	105,106	ROM.	15:1-20
17	PS.	107,108	ROM.	15:21-33
18	PS.	109,110,111	ROM.	16
19	PS.	112-115	I COR.	1
20	PS.	116-118	I COR.	2
21	PS.	119:1-48	I COR.	3
22	PS.	119:49-104	I COR.	4
23	PS.	119:105-176	I COR.	5
24	PS.	120-123	I COR.	6
25	PS.	124-127	I COR.	7:1-24
26	PS.	128-131	I COR.	7:25-40
27	PS.	132-135	I COR.	8
28	PS.	136-138	I COR.	9
29	PS.	139-141	I COR.	10:1-13
30	PS.	142-144	I COR.	10:14-33
31	PS.	145-147	I COR.	11:1-15

SEPTEMBER

DATE	MORNING		EVENING	
1	PS.	148-150	I COR.	11:16-34
2	PROV.	1,2	I COR.	12
3	PROV.	3,4	I COR.	13
4	PROV.	5,6	I COR.	14:1-20
5	PROV.	7,8	I COR.	14:21-40
6	PROV.	9,10	I COR.	15:1-32
7	PROV.	11,12	I COR.	15:33-58
8	PROV.	13,14	I COR.	16
9	PROV.	15,16	II COR.	1
10	PROV.	17,18	II COR.	2
11	PROV.	19,20	II COR.	3
12	PROV.	21,22	II COR.	4
13	PROV.	23,24	II COR.	5
14	PROV.	25,26,27	II COR.	6
15	PROV.	28,29	II COR.	7
16	PROV.	30,31	II COR.	8
17	ECCLES.	1,2,3	II COR.	9
18	ECCLES.	4,5,6	II COR.	10
19	ECCLES.	7,8,9	II COR.	11:1-15
20	ECCLES.	10,11,12	II COR.	11:16-33
21	SOL.	1,2,3	II COR.	12
22	SOL.	4,5	II COR.	13
23	SOL.	6,7,8	GAL.	1
24	ISA.	1,2,3	GAL.	2
25	ISA.	4,5,6	GAL.	3
26	ISA.	7,8,9	GAL.	4
27	ISA.	10,11,12	GAL.	5
28	ISA.	13,14,15	GAL.	6
29	ISA.	16,17,18	EPH.	1
30	ISA.	19,20,21	EPH.	2

NOVEMBER

DATE	MORNING		EVENING	
1	JER.	31,32	TITUS	2
2	JER.	33,34,35	TITUS	3
3	JER.	36,37	PHILEM.	
4	JER.	38,39	HEB.	1
5	JER.	40,41,42	HEB.	2
6	JER.	43,44,45	HEB.	3
7	JER.	46,47,48	HEB.	4
8	JER.	49,50	HEB.	5
9	JER.	51,52	HEB.	6
10	LAM.	1,2	HEB.	7
11	LAM.	3,4,5	HEB.	8
12	EZEK.	1,2,3	HEB.	9
13	EZEK.	4,5,6	HEB.	10:1-23
14	EZEK.	7,8,9	HEB.	10:24-39
15	EZEK.	10,11,12	HEB.	11:1-19
16	EZEK.	13,14,15	HEB.	11:20-40
17	EZEK.	16	HEB.	12
18	EZEK.	17,18,19	HEB.	13
19	EZEK.	20,21	JAS.	1
20	EZEK.	22,23	JAS.	2
21	EZEK.	24,25,26	JAS.	3
22	EZEK.	27,28	JAS.	4
23	EZEK.	29,30,31	JAS.	5
24	EZEK.	32,33	I PET.	1
25	EZEK.	34,35	I PET.	2
26	EZEK.	36,37	I PET.	3
27	EZEK.	38,39	I PET.	4
28	EZEK.	40	I PET.	5
29	EZEK.	41,42	II PET.	1
30	EZEK.	43,44	II PET.	2

OCTOBER

DATE	MORNING		EVENING	
1	ISA.	22,23	EPH.	3
2	ISA.	24,25,26	EPH.	4
3	ISA.	27,28	EPH.	5
4	ISA.	29,30	EPH.	6
5	ISA.	31,32,33	PHIL.	1
6	ISA.	34,35,36	PHIL.	2
7	ISA.	37,38	PHIL.	3
8	ISA.	39,40	PHIL.	4
9	ISA.	41,42	COL.	1
10	ISA.	43,44	COL.	2
11	ISA.	45,46,47	COL.	3
12	ISA.	48,49	COL.	4
13	ISA.	50,51,52	I THESS.	1
14	ISA.	53,54,55	I THESS.	2
15	ISA.	56,57,58	I THESS.	3
16	ISA.	59,60,61	I THESS.	4
17	ISA.	62,63,64	I THESS.	5
18	ISA.	65,66	II THESS.	1
19	JER.	1,2	II THESS.	2
20	JER.	3,4	II THESS.	3
21	JER.	5,6	I TIM.	1
22	JER.	7,8	I TIM.	2
23	JER.	9,10	I TIM.	3
24	JER.	11,12,13	I TIM.	4
25	JER.	14,15,16	I TIM.	5
26	JER.	17,18,19	I TIM.	6
27	JER.	20,21,22	II TIM.	1
28	JER.	23,24	II TIM.	2
29	JER.	25,26	II TIM.	3
30	JER.	27,28	II TIM.	4
31	JER.	29,30	TITUS	1

DECEMBER

DATE	MORNING		EVENING	
1	EZEK.	45,46	II PET.	3
2	EZEK.	47,48	I JOHN	1
3	DAN.	1,2	I JOHN	2
4	DAN.	3,4	I JOHN	3
5	DAN.	5,6	I JOHN	4
6	DAN.	7,8	I JOHN	5
7	DAN.	9,10	II JOHN	
8	DAN.	11,12	III JOHN	
9	HOS.	1-4	JUDE	
10	HOS.	5-8	REV.	1
11	HOS.	9,10,11	REV.	2
12	HOS.	12,13,14	REV.	3
13	JOEL	1,2,3	REV.	4
14	AMOS	1,2,3	REV.	5
15	AMOS	4,5,6	REV.	6
16	AMOS	7,8,9	REV.	7
17	OBAD.		REV.	8
18	JONAH		REV.	9
19	MIC.	1,2,3	REV.	10
20	MIC.	4,5	REV	11
21	MIC.	6,7	REV.	12
22	NAH.		REV.	13
23	HAB.		REV.	14
24	ZEPH.		REV.	15
25	HAG.		REV.	16
26	ZECH.	1,2,3	REV.	17
27	ZECH.	4,5,6	REV.	18
28	ZECH.	7,8,9	REV.	19
29	ZECH	10,11,12	REV.	20
30	ZECH.	13,14	REV.	21
31	MAL.		REV.	22

SCRIPTURE MEMORY REVIEW

Week	Scripture Reference	Week	Scripture Reference
1		8	
2		9	
3		10	
4		11	
5		12	
6		13	
7			

Additional Verses

CHURCH FRIENDS LIST

Name	Address	Phone

NEXT ACT ON MY PART
l letter
p phone call
v personal visit
o other

ADDITIONAL AIDS

QUIET TIME HIGHLIGHTS

Date	Insight

PERSONAL MINISTRY ACTIVITIES
FOR THE MONTH OF _____

PERSONAL MINISTRY ACTIVITIES
FOR THE MONTH OF _____

	SUNDAY	MONDAY	TUESDAY	WEDNESDAY	THURSDAY	FRIDAY	SATURDAY

PERSONAL MINISTRY ACTIVITIES
FOR THE MONTH OF _____

SUNDAY	MONDAY	TUESDAY	WEDNESDAY	THURSDAY	FRIDAY	SATURDAY

ADDITIONAL AIDS

PERSONAL MINISTRY ACTIVITIES
FOR THE MONTH OF _____

SUNDAY	MONDAY	TUESDAY	WEDNESDAY	THURSDAY	FRIDAY	SATURDAY